NICK JR
DORA the EXPLORER

Dora's Garden Adventure

¡Hola! Boots and I are going on a great adventure today to help our friend Isa save her garden. Read along and you can join us! You will know it is time to turn the page when you hear this sound.... Are you ready? ¡Vámonos!

Story Reader

publications international, ltd.

¡Hola! I'm Dora and this is my best friend, Boots. We're going to Isa's Flowery Garden to help Isa! Everything in her garden is growing too big! The sunflowers almost reach the sun! To make everything the right size again, Isa needs this watering can full of magic water...and fast!

We need to find the quickest way to Isa's Flowery Garden.

Who do we ask for help when we don't know which way to go?

 The Map! The Map can tell us the quickest way to get to Isa's Flowery Garden! Will you check the Map? You have to say Map!

 Say Map! Say Map!

 Map says we need to go past the Froggy Pond and through the Spooky Forest, and that's how we get to Isa's Flowery Garden. Come on! *¡Vámonos!*

First, we need to find the Froggy Pond. Do you see the Froggy Pond? There it is! Let's go!

We made it to the Froggy Pond! But how are we going to get all the way across the Froggy Pond? Let's stop and think. Do you see anything that will help us get across?

One. Two. Three. Four. Five. Six. Seven!
We made it across the Froggy Pond! Thanks for helping.

Now we need to go to the Spooky Forest. Do you see the Spooky Forest? There it is! And there's our friend Tico! He can give us a ride through the Spooky Forest on his bicycle. Will you help us tell Tico to wait? Tico speaks Spanish, so we need to say *¡Espera!* Say it with us!
¡Espera! ¡Espera!

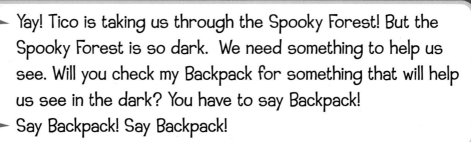

Yay! Tico is taking us through the Spooky Forest! But the Spooky Forest is so dark. We need something to help us see. Will you check my Backpack for something that will help us see in the dark? You have to say Backpack!

Say Backpack! Say Backpack!

Do you see something that we can use to see in the dark?

We can use the flashlight to see in the dark! Good thinking. Did you hear that? That sounds like Swiper the fox. Boots, we better watch out.

That sneaky fox is always trying to swipe our stuff.

Oh, no! Swiper will try to swipe our flashlight! Do you see Swiper? Where?

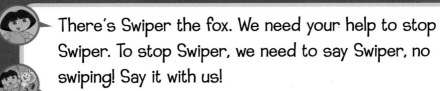

There's Swiper the fox. We need your help to stop Swiper. To stop Swiper, we need to say Swiper, no swiping! Say it with us!

Swiper, no swiping! Swiper, no swiping! Swiper, no swiping!

Oh, man!

We did it! We stopped Swiper. Thanks for helping. Now we'll be able to get through the Spooky Forest.

18

Wow! The Spooky Forest has lots of animals. Look at the bats and crocodiles and snakes. We better hurry through the Spooky Forest. We need the path that will lead us out of the Spooky Forest. Do you see the path that we can take?

We made it out of the Spooky Forest. *Gracias*, Tico!

De nada.

Look, there's Isa's Flowery Garden!

Everything's so big! Come on! *¡Vámonos!*